Get ready for the KS1 SATs with CGP!

This CGP SAT Buster is the perfect way to help pupils prepare for the KS1 Grammar, Punctuation and Spelling SATs Test in 2017 and beyond! It's packed full of friendly questions to build up all the skills they'll need.

It also includes self-assessment tick boxes so that pupils can make a note of how confident they feel about each topic — ideal for keeping track of their progress.

What CGP is all about

Our sole aim here at CGP is to produce the highest quality books — carefully written, immaculately presented and dangerously close to being funny.

Then we work our socks off to get them out to you — at the cheapest possible prices.

Contents

Published by CGP

Editors: Joanna Daniels, Alex Fairer and Holly Robinson

With thanks to Emma Crighton and Anne James for the proofreading.

ISBN: 978 1 78294 709 7

Clipart from Corel®
Printed by Elanders Ltd, Newcastle upon Tyne.
Based on the classic CGP style created by Richard Parsons.

Nouns

1. Put a **tick** next to the word which is a **noun**.

Sam thought the cake was really tasty.

Tick **one** box.

thought ☐

cake ☑

really ☐

tasty ☐

2. **Circle** the **two nouns** in the sentence below.

The   little   monkey   climbed   up   the   tree.

3. Complete the sentence with a **noun** from the list.

big   quickly   field   farming

Karen ran through the ....field................ full of cows.

Are you as happy as a Spellephant?

Noun phrases

1. Put a tick next to the noun phrase.

Tick **one** box.

he ran around the park ☑

an exciting trip ☑

the hamster escaped ☒

she collected her parcel ☐

2. Write a word on each line below to complete the noun phrases.

the warm ....

the lazy ....

a happy ....dog....................

3. Circle the noun phrases below.

slithering snake   often careless   look out

the scary roller coaster   go away

Spellephants love noun phrases. Do you?

Verbs

1. **Circle** the **verb** in the sentence below.

   They (listened) to the music together.

2. **Circle** all the **verbs** below.

   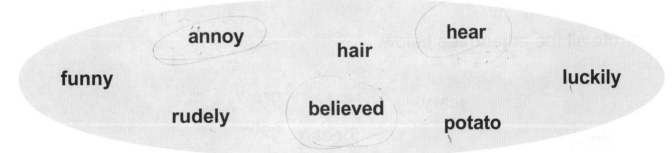

   funny   (annoy)   hair   (hear)   luckily

   rudely   (believed)   potato

3. **Tick one** box to show which word is a **verb**.

   The parrot hopped onto the pirate's shoulder.

4. **Find** and **copy two verbs** from the sentence below.

   Joe read the library books and then returned them.

   read   returned

Adjectives

1. **Tick one** box to show which word is an **adjective**.

The thief stole the beautiful painting from the gallery.

☐ ☐ ☑ ☐

2. **Circle** all the **adjectives** below.

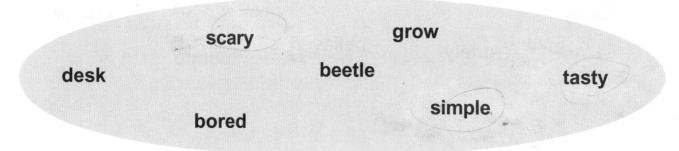

desk   scary   grow   beetle   tasty   simple   bored

3. **Circle** the **adjective** in the sentence below.

He had a snack because he was hungry.

4. Complete the sentence with an **adjective** from the list.

piece   enjoy   big   chocolate

Peter helped himself to a .... slice of cake.

Are you as skilful as a Spellephant?

Adverbs

1. Tick **one** box to show which word is an **adverb**.

The man ran quickly down the hill.

↑ ☐ ↑ ☐ ↑ ☑ ↑ ☐

2. **Circle** the **adverb** in the sentence below.

Jane sang (quietly) in the shower.

3. Complete the sentence with an **adverb** from the list.

excitedly   **noise**   **shout**   **big**

The crowd cheered .... when the team won.

4. Put **ticks** next to the words that are **adverbs**.

old ☐   ticked ☐   softly ☐

clock ☐   noisily ☑   listened ☐

Did you make quick work of adverbs?

Sentences

1. Put a **tick** next to the **complete** sentence.

Tick **one** box.

I wrote her a letter bought a stamp posted it. ☐

I love my favourite jumper, stripy and warm. ☐

The rain had stopped and the sun was out. ☑

Chelsea couldn't remember the keys were. ☐

2. Draw **lines** to match the first half of each sentence to its second half.

They put	the bucket full of water.
He filled	the tinsel on the tree.
We are	going to the zoo.

3. **Rearrange** the words below into a sentence that makes sense. Then **add** a capital letter and a full stop in the correct places.

very   **was**   **lake**   **cold**   **the**

....

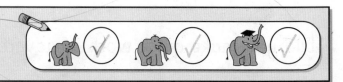

Are your sentences up to scratch?

 **Types of sentences**

1. Read the sentence below.
    Tick one box to show what **type** of sentence it is.

    ### Charlie's mum is making pasta.

    command ☐   exclamation ☑   question ☐   statement ☐

2. **Write** down what **type** of sentence each of the following are.

    Can you fix my bike?   ....

    What a great bike I have!   ....

3. Draw **lines** to match each sentence to the correct label.

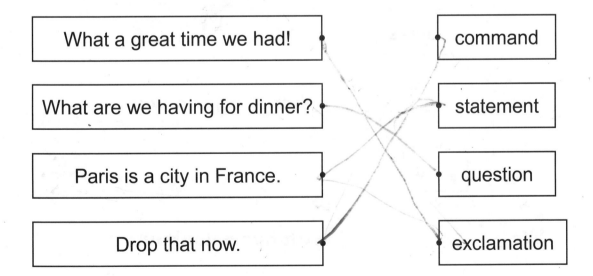

What a great time we had!	command
What are we having for dinner?	statement
Paris is a city in France.	question
Drop that now.	exclamation

Are you as splendid as a Spellephant?

Simple past and simple present tenses

1. **Circle** the correct words so that each sentence is in the **present tense**.

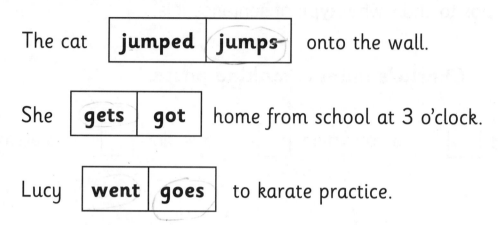

The cat | jumped | ~~jumps~~ | onto the wall.

She | gets | got | home from school at 3 o'clock.

Lucy | went | goes | to karate practice.

2. The words in the boxes are in the present tense. Fill in the gaps by writing these words in the **simple past tense**. One has already been done for you.

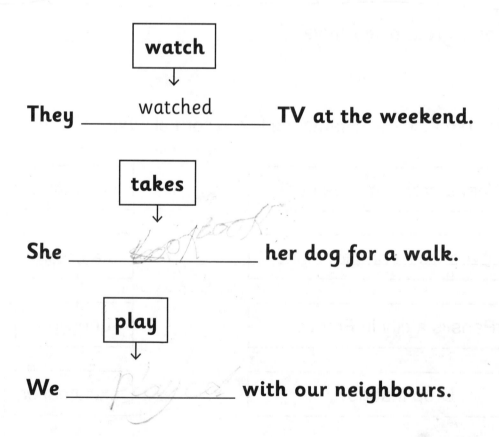

watch

They _____watched_____ **TV at the weekend.**

takes

She _____ **her dog for a walk.**

play

We _____ **with our neighbours.**

'ing' verbs

1. Complete the sentence with the correct **verb** from the list.

ran   **running**   **runs**   **run**

They could see that someone was .... up the hill.

2. **Circle** the correct verbs to complete the sentences.

The dog is | **barked** | **barking** | . It is | **trying** | **tried** | to

wake up its owner.

3. Put a **tick** to show whether each sentence is in the **past** or **present tense**.

sentence	present tense	past tense
Charlie was feeding the hens.	✓	
I am saving my money.		✓
They were diving into the water.	✓	

Spellephants love verbs. Do you?

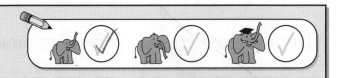

Section 1 — Grammar

Using the right verb form

1. Circle the correct verb form to complete this sentence.

He [**kicked** | **kicking**] the ball to his team mate.

2. Put a **tick** next to the sentence that is **correct**.

Tick **one** box.

I are trying to learn French. ☐

I have trying to learn French. ☐

I am trying to learn French. ☐

I is trying to learn French. ☐

3. Draw **lines** to match each sentence to the correct verb form.

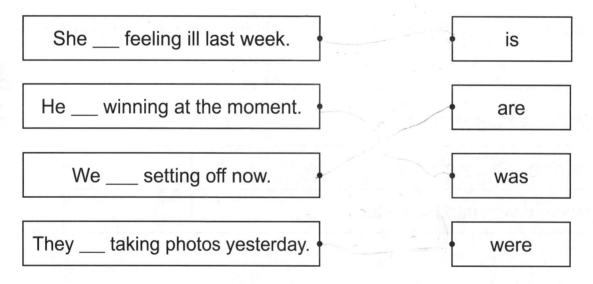

She ___ feeling ill last week.	is
He ___ winning at the moment.	are
We ___ setting off now.	was
They ___ taking photos yesterday.	were

Do you use verbs like a Spellephant?

Staying in the same tense

1. **Circle** the verb from the list below which completes the sentence.

   The bird _____ above the trees before it landed on a branch.

   fly   **flying**   **flown**   **flew**

2. **Circle** the correct options to complete the sentences.

   Colin went to the zoo and | **saw** | **sees** | some penguins.

   It is getting dark and the snow | **was falling** | **is falling** | heavily.

3. Put a **tick** next to the sentence that is **correct**.

   Tick **one** box.

   They sit down and eats.   ☐

   They sat down and eat.   ☐

   They sit down and eaten.   ☐

   They sat down and ate.   ☐

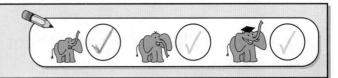

Are you as spiffing as a Spellephant?

Section 1 — Grammar

and, or, but

1. **Circle** the correct word from the list below to complete the sentence.

I could either go swimming _____ I could play netball.

(or)   **but**   **and**

2. Put a **tick** next to the sentence that uses joining words **correctly**.

Tick **one** box.

Clive wanted to go or see the ruined castle. ☐

I enjoy living in the city but Amy prefers living in the countryside. ☐

We could either have fish and pasta for tea. ☑

Tina hates shopping or she needed to buy new clothes. ☐

3. **Write** a joining word in the gap to complete the sentence.

I want to go to Japan ....but........... my parents don't like flying.

Are you as skilled as a Spellephant?

when, if, that, because

1. **Circle** the joining word in the sentence below.

   Carl was in trouble (because) he broke the vase.

2. **Circle** the missing joining word in the sentence from the list below.

   Martina painted the fence _____ that _____ she built yesterday.

   if   (**that**)   (**because**)

3. Draw **lines** to match each sentence to the correct joining word.
   Use each option **once**.

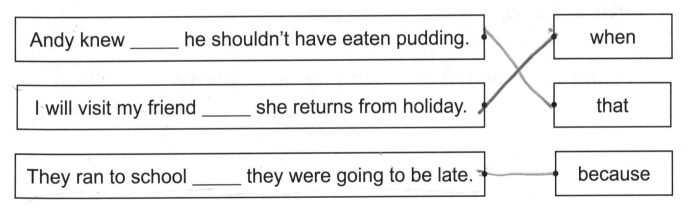

Andy knew _____ he shouldn't have eaten pudding.		when
I will visit my friend _____ she returns from holiday.		that
They ran to school _____ they were going to be late.		because

4. **Write** a joining word in the gap to complete the sentence.

   Faye wonders .... that .... the moon is made of cheese.

Are you a joining word genius?

Section 1 — Grammar

Mixed practice

1. **Circle** the **adverb** in the sentence below.

   The elephant played happily in the river.

2. **Find** and **copy** the **joining word** from the sentence below.

   She wasn't sure when her aunt was supposed to be arriving.

   ....

3. **Circle** all the **adjectives** in the box below.

calm	pencil	cloudy	pretty	flew

4. Draw **lines** to match each sentence to the correct **joining word**.

The hens are either eating _____ they're sleeping.		but
I was confused by the map _____ I felt very lost.		and
She wanted to go to the party _____ she was too tired.		or

Mixed practice

5. Read the sentence below. Tick **one** box to show what type of sentence it is.

Go to the shops.

command ☐   exclamation ☐   statement ☐   question ☑

6. Put a **tick** next to the word which completes the sentence.

Mo knew that Tyson was _____ **at the card game.**

cheats ☐   cheating ☑

cheat ☐   cheater ☐

7. Put a **tick** next to the sentence which is in the **past tense**.

Their garden looks lovely. ☐   The plane is flying overhead. ☐

I chose my sandwich filling. ☐   The sheep are grazing. ☐

Are you a master of mixed practice?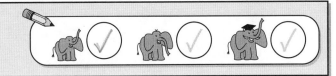

Section 1 — Grammar

Section 2 — Punctuation

Capital letters

1. The sentence below is missing a **capital letter**.
   Tick **one** box to show where the capital letter should go.

   Sam had a glass of water and i had some lemonade.

2. Put a **tick** next to the sentence that uses **capital letters** correctly.

   Tick **one** box.

   on Friday, he went to the dentist. ☐

   on friday, he went to the dentist. ☐

   On Friday, he went to the dentist. ☐

   On friday, he went to the dentist. ☐

3. **Circle** all the words below that need **capital letters**.

   sarah   germany   apple   scotland   after   slowly   monday   easy

Capital letters

4. **Circle** the words in the sentence below that should have **capital letters**.

we are going on holiday to paris on tuesday.

5. **Tick** each row to show whether each sentence uses **capital letters** **correctly** or **incorrectly**.

sentence	correctly	incorrectly
We're going to Ben's house tomorrow.	✓	
Rachel liked the drawing I did.	✓	
We make a roast dinner every sunday.		✗
Olive went to the Shops in the morning.		✗

6. Read the sentence below.
   Why do the three underlined words start with **capital letters**?

   I sat next to <u>Tanisha</u> on the way to <u>London</u> last <u>Saturday</u>.

   because ....

   ....

   day or name. and Tanisha is a

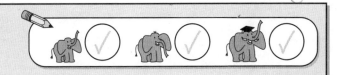

Are you as super as a Spellephant?

Section 2 — Punctuation

Ending sentences

1. The sentence below is missing a **punctuation mark**.
   Add the correct punctuation mark.

Why were you late to school today

2. The sentences below are missing a **full stop**.
   Tick **one** box to show where the full stop should go.

Today is my birthday I got lots of cards and presents.

3. **Tick** each row to show whether each sentence should end with
   a **question mark** or an **exclamation mark**.

sentence	?	!
What is your favourite colour	✓	
How wonderful you look	✓	✓
Where are my shoes	✓	
What a great idea that is		✓

Ending sentences

4. Draw **lines** to match each sentence with
   the **most likely** final punctuation mark.

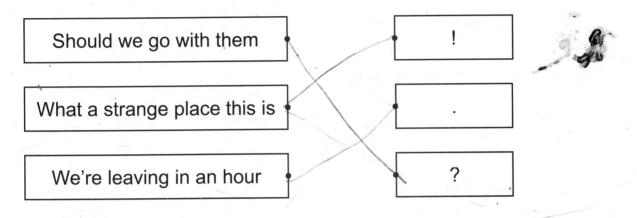

Should we go with them		!
What a strange place this is		.
We're leaving in an hour		?

5. Read the sentences below and **circle** the **full stops** that are **wrong**.

   Harry's school shoes. had a hole in them. He needed
   a new pair because. his feet would get wet if it rained.
   His sister. Lisa had the same problem with her shoes.

6. **Add** the correct **punctuation mark** to the sentences below.

   Are they bringing their new puppy........

   How incredible this pizza is........

   Jane enjoys cycling........

Do you end sentences like a Spellephant?

Section 2 — Punctuation

Apostrophes

1. Put a **tick** next to the sentence that uses an **apostrophe correctly**.

Tick **one** box.

Jacks cakes tasted deliciou's. ☐

Jack's cakes tasted delicious. ☑

Jacks cake's tasted delicious. ☐

Jacks cakes' tasted delicious. ☐

2. **Circle** the words which use **apostrophes** correctly.

The red jacket is | **Sophies** | **Sophie's** | .

I think | **they'll** | **the'yll** | be here soon.

3. **Match** the groups of words together that mean the **same thing**.

| I am | | don't |

| do not | | they've |

| they have | | I'm |

Apostrophes

4. The sentence below is missing an **apostrophe**.
Tick one box to show where the apostrophe should go.

Ross and Ben sat on Carols couch to eat their sandwiches.

5. The sentence below is missing one **apostrophe**.
Circle the word that should have an apostrophe.

We took lots of pictures at my grandmas party.

6. Write the underlined words in their **short form** using an **apostrophe**.

Ryan said he <u>could not</u> find his keys.

....

7. Read the sentence below.
Why do the **underlined** words need apostrophes?

I <u>should've</u> gone to bed earlier but I <u>didn't</u> feel tired.

....

....

Have you mastered apostrophes?

Commas

1. **Tick one** box to show where a comma should go.

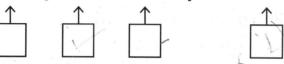

I had a pie some crisps and an orange.

☐   ☐   ☐   ☐

2. Put a **tick** next to the sentence that uses a **comma correctly**.

Tick **one** box.

He said he wanted a black silver or, blue tie.   ☐

I like football tennis, and rugby.   ☐

Tim, Andrew and Janey ordered a pizza.   ☑

We could get, a bus the train or a taxi.   ☐

3. The sentences below are each missing **one comma**.
   Write a comma in the correct place.

The hotel had a pool, a gym and a restaurant.

Chris Charlotte and Anna went on a bike ride.

Can you use commas like a Spellephant?

Mixed practice

1. **Circle** the name of the **punctuation mark** that
   shows that a sentence is **asking** something.

comma   exclamation mark

full stop   apostrophe

question mark

2. Put a **tick** next to the punctuation mark that is missing from this sentence.

I enjoyed the concert last night

Tick **one** box.

apostrophe ☐

comma ☐

question mark ☐

full stop ☑

3. **Circle** the words in the sentence below that should have **capital letters**.

she told me callum gave her the present on monday.

Mixed practice

4. Put a **tick** next to the sentence that uses an **apostrophe correctly**.

Tick **one** box.

She has'nt had any breakfast yet. ☐

She hasnt' had any breakfast yet. ☐

She hasn't had any breakfast yet. ☐

She ha'snt had any breakfast yet. ☐

5. Put **ticks** next to **two** sentences that use **capital letters** correctly.

Tick **two** boxes.

Their cat is called oliver. ☐

They are moving to America next month. ☑

We need to finish our homework by Thursday. ☐

She asked if i needed help. ☐

6. The sentence below is missing **one comma**.
    Write a comma in the correct place.

    The knives forks and spoons are in the top drawer.

Mixed practice

7. **Circle two** words in this sentence that should have apostrophes.

She promised she (wouldn't) tell (anyone) (Molly's) secret.

8. Add a **question mark** or an **exclamation mark** to each of these sentences.

Where are you going...?.   What time is it...?.

What nice hair you have...!.   How frustrating this is...!...

9. **Tick** each row to show whether each sentence uses **commas** **correctly** or **incorrectly**.

sentence	correctly	incorrectly
We need bread, eggs, and milk.		✓
Jamie, Rosie and Sam, are best friends.	✗	✗ ✓
Should we use green, red or blue, paint?		
You can have juice, water or tea.	✓	

Spellephants love punctuation. Do you?

Suffixes — plurals

1. **Tick** each row to show whether each word is **singular** or **plural**.

word	singular	plural
rabbit	✓	
matches		✓
eggs		✓
house	✓	

2. Draw **lines** to match each word to the **suffix** needed to make it a **plural**.

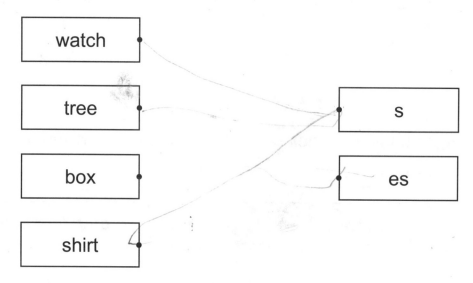

3. **Circle** all the **singular words** below.

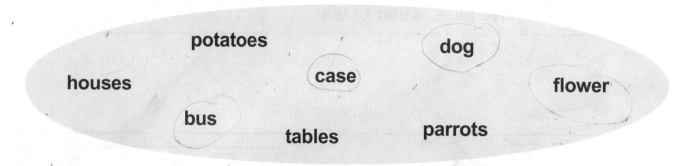

Suffixes — plurals

4. Put a **tick** next to the option that uses **plurals correctly**.

Tick **one** box.

I own three pet. I have two dogs and a cat. ☐

I own three pets. I have two dog and a cat. ☐

I own three pets. I have two dogs and a cats. ☐

I own three pets. I have two dogs and a cat. ☐

5. **Complete** the sentence with the **plural** of the word below.

party

All the girls had birthday ....

6. What is the **difference** in meaning between the **two words** below?

animal   **animals**

....

....

Do you know plurals like a Spellephant?

Suffixes — other endings

1. Draw **lines** to match each word to the **suffix** that can be used to make a **new word**. One has already been done for you.

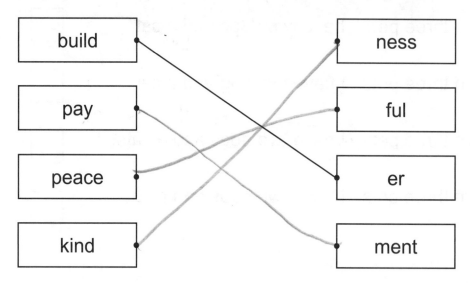

build	ness
pay	ful
peace	er
kind	ment

2. **Tick two suffixes** which can be added to the word **care**.

less ☑   ment ☐   ness ☑   ⁻ful ☑

3. **Circle** all the **suffixes** that can be added to the word **soft**.

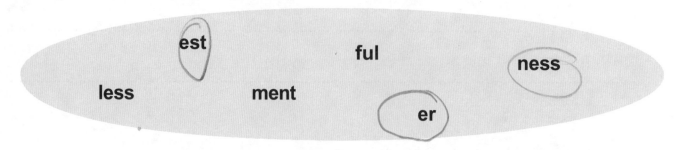

est   ful   ness
less   ment   er

Suffixes — other endings

4. **Tick** each row to show which **suffix** can be added to each word.

word	ment	ful
enjoy	✓	
help		✓
forget	✓	✓
move	✓	

5. **Circle** the word with the **correct suffix** in each sentence.

The group came to an | **agreeness** | **agreement** |.

She went to the doctor about her | **illness** | **illful** |.

She felt very | **cheerest** | **cheerful** | when it was her birthday.

6. **Write** a **suffix** at the end of the word **breath** to complete the sentence below.

    less   **ment**   **ness**   **er**

She felt breath...*less*... after running up the stairs.

Spellephants love suffixes. Do you?

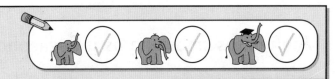

Adding 'un' to words

1. Add a **prefix** to these words so they have the **opposite meaning**.

    ....*un*..........**well**   ....*un*..........**sure**   ....*un*..........**happy**

2. **Circle** all the words below that you can add the **prefix 'un'** to.

lift

equal

speak

likely

dry

place

run

pack

3. **Circle** the word in this sentence that means the opposite of **fair**.

    Emma had to wash the dishes by herself. She thought it was unfair because no one else helped.

4. Read the sentence below.
    He was kind to his friends.

    Add a **prefix** to the word kind so that the sentence means the **opposite**.

    He was ....*un*..........**kind to his friends.**

Compound words

1. **Circle** the **compound word** in this sentence.

   She was looking for the hammer in the (toolbox.)

2. Draw **lines** to match the words that can be **joined** to make new words. One has already been done for you.

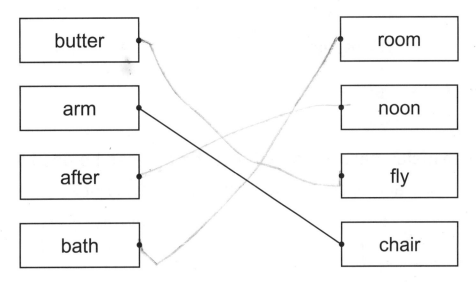

butter	room
arm	noon
after	fly
bath	chair

3. Use each word **once** to **complete** the passage below.

   brush   **ball**   **over**

   I am going to my friend's house for a sleep......................... tonight.

   I will need to pack my tooth......................... We will probably play

   foot......................... for a while when I get there.

Can you make words like a Spellephant?

Section 3

Mixed practice

1. Which of these words can have the **prefix 'un'** added to it?

    Tick **one** box.

    take   ☐

    drop   ☐

    fasten   ☐

    repeat   ☐

2. Draw **lines** to match each word to the **suffix** that can be used to make a **new word**. Use each option **once**. One has already been done for you.

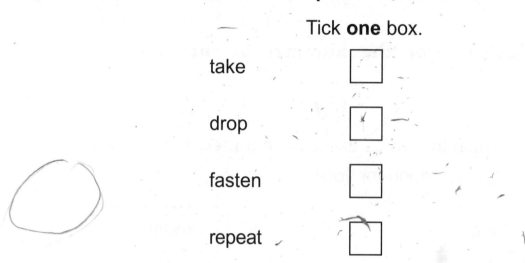

pain	ness
treat	er
farm	ment
polite	ful

3. **Circle two** words that can be joined to make a **new word**.

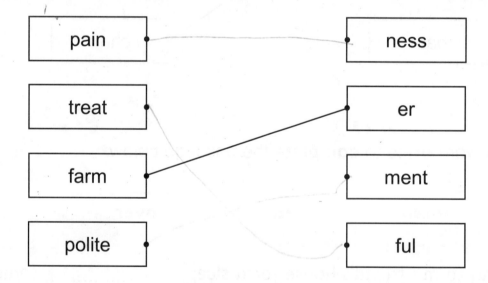

     line   wall   snow   paper

Mixed practice

4. **Cross out** the **wrong word** in each sentence.

The sailors all wore blue | ~~hates~~ | hats |.

He had to catch three | ~~buss~~ | buses | to get there.

They got some new | dishes | ~~dishs~~ | as a present.

5. Add 'less' or 'est' to make each of these words into a **new word**.

spot............   deep............

quick............   power............

6. **Complete** the table by writing the **plurals** of the **singular words**.

singular	plural
baby	babies
fly	flies
ferry	
family	

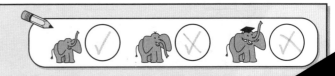

Are you spiffing like a Spellephant?

Section 4 — Spelling

Vowel sounds

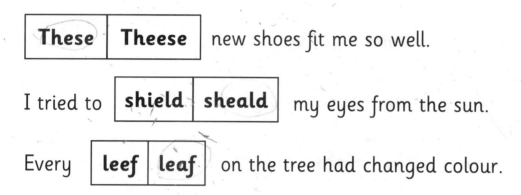

1. **Circle** the **correct** spelling in each sentence below.

   | These | Theese | new shoes fit me so well.

   I tried to | shield | sheald | my eyes from the sun.

   Every | leef | leaf | on the tree had changed colour.

2. Draw **lines** to match each gap with the correct missing letters.

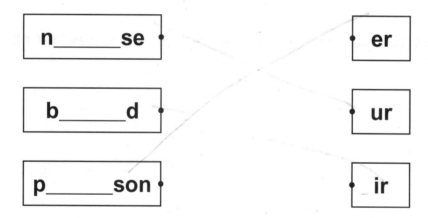

n_____se   er

b_____d   ur

p_____son   ir

3. **Tick** to show which words are spelt **wrongly**.

   The waiter carried the drinks on a traye to our table.

   Our main meals caim afterwards. They were taysty.

Vocabulary

...elling

Vowel sounds

4. **Write** either '**oi**' or '**oy**' in each gap below to complete the sentences.

    Layla paid the shopkeeper with a pound **c**............**n**.

    The sharp **p**............**nt** on my pencil broke off.

    We visited the **r**............**al** palace on a school trip.

    Sue couldn't hide her **j**............ when she won the tennis match.

5. **Circle** the word in each pair that is spelt **correctly**.

    ride / righed   trighed / tried

    lyke / like   dryd / dried

6. Draw **lines** from each word to the correct box in the middle.

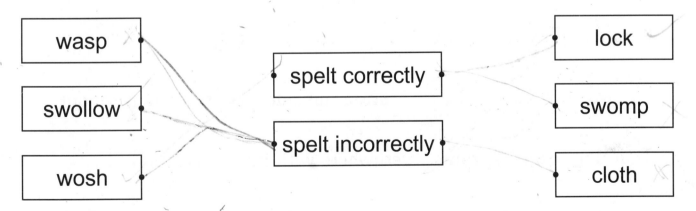

Vowel sounds

7. **Circle** the **correct** spelling from each pair of words below.

yawn / yorn   corl / call   tork / talk   award / awored

8. **Circle** the words below that are spelt **correctly**.

tirm	term	turm

berst	birst	burst

shert	shurt	shirt

her	hur	hir

curl	cirl	cerl

furst	ferst	first

9. **Circle** the **correct** spelling in each sentence below.

Kyra hung her wet **coat / cowt** up on the peg.

Lou was excited to **show / shoe** his dad the fish he had caught.

That dog **goas / goes** everywhere with his owner.

Vowel sounds

10. Draw **lines** to match each gap with either '**ou**' or '**ow**'.
    One has already been done for you.

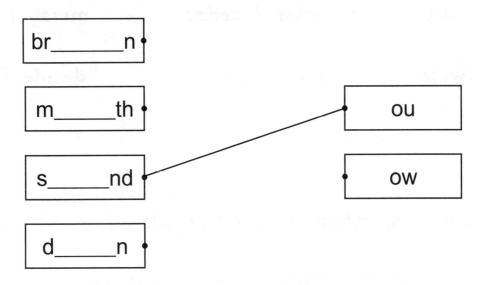

br_____n

m_____th

s_____nd ——— ou

ow

d_____n

11. Write either '**oo**', '**ue**' or '**ew**' in each gap below to complete the sentence.

The **m**...........**n** looks very bright tonight.

Lily **thr**............. the ball to me but I dropped it.

My dad had to **resc**............. a bird that flew into our house.

12. Write either '**air**', '**ear**' or '**are**' in each gap below to complete the sentences.

He sat on the **ch**...............   I decided to **w**............... shorts.

I have a new toy **b**...............   You should **sh**............... the cake.

Are you as super as a Spellephant?

The soft 'c' sound

1. **Circle** the **correct** spelling from each pair of words below.

    chest / chect   sellar / cellar   mersy / mercy

    twise / twice   trust / truct   decide / deside

2. **Circle** the **correct** spelling in each sentence below.

    I watched Dad make the **icing / ising** for the cake.

    Jim forgot to take his shopping **lict / list** with him.

    She came to school on a **fansy / fancy** new scooter.

3. **Write** either 's' or 'c' to complete the words below.

    ....elery   ex..........ited   ra..........e

    spi..........y   hor..........e   si..........ter

Are you as successful as a Spellephant?

The hard 'c' sound

1. Tick to show which word is spelt **wrongly**.

The shepherd kept kounting the sheep in his flock.

2. Draw **lines** to match each gap with the correct **hard 'c'** sound.

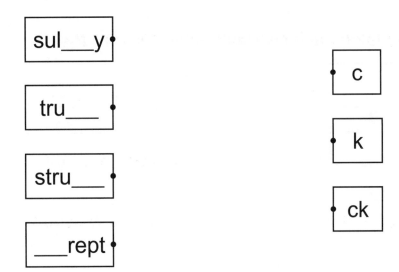

3. **Write** either '**c**', '**k**' or '**ck**' in each gap below to complete the sentence.

They wished me good **lu**.......... before the show.

I ate strawberries and ....**ream** for my dessert.

Rowan told me a very funny **jo**..........**e** but I can't remember it.

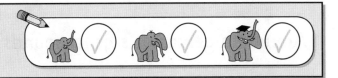

The soft 'g' sound

1. **Circle** all the words below that have **soft 'g'** sounds.

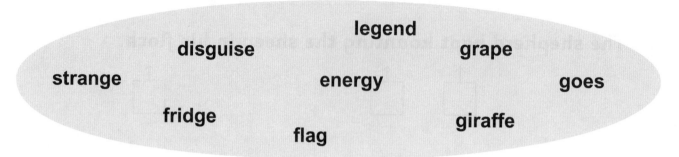

legend

disguise

grape

strange

energy

goes

fridge

giraffe

flag

2. Draw **lines** to match each gap with either '**ge**' or '**dge**'.

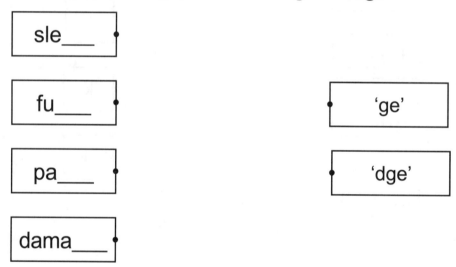

sle___

fu___

'ge'

pa___

'dge'

dama___

3. Circle the words that are spelt **incorrectly** in the sentences below.

Becca tried to dodge a lardge, angry seagull. It chardged

at her, and pecked her with its huge orange beak.

Are you a genius at soft 'g' sounds?

Silent letters

1. **Circle** the silent letter in each word below.

   g n o m e   **w r e c k**   **k n u c k l e**   **w r i t e r**

2. **Tick** the **four** silent letters in the sentence below.

   The brave **k**night **w**rapped the dragon's **t**ail **a**round the

   ↑   ↑   ↑ ↑
   □   □   □ □

   pillar and **k**notted it so that he **c**ouldn't **w**riggle **f**ree.

   ↑   ↑   ↑   ↑
   □   □   □   □

3. **Write** either '**g**', '**k**' or '**w**' in each gap below to complete the sentence.

   Simon wanted to watch the ....**restling** match.

   The ....**nat** kept flying around my head.

   We took a ....**rong** turn and got very lost.

Section 4 — Spelling

Words with 'tch'

1. **Circle** the **correct** spelling from each pair of words below.

   teatch / teach   butcher / bucher   beatch / beach

2. **Circle** the words that are spelt **incorrectly** in the sentence below.

   Lucy was sketching a bird. It was perched on a brantch

   but then it streched its wings and flew away.

3. Draw **lines** to match each gap with either '**ch**' or '**tch**'.
   One has already been done for you.

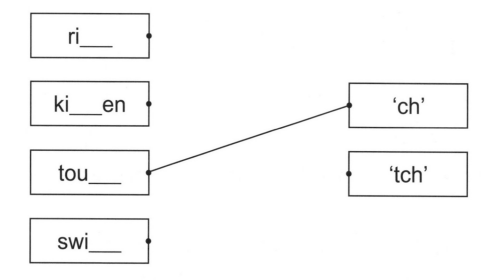

4. **Write** either '**tch**' or '**ch**' in each gap below to complete the word.

   twi...............   pi...............   su...............

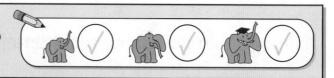

Spellephants love 'tch' sounds. Do you?

'wh' and 'ph' words

1. **Circle** the word that is spelt **incorrectly**.

   wheat   phrog   orphan   whale

2. **Circle** the **correct** spelling from each pair of words below.

   wind / whind   nefew / nephew   trophy / trofy

3. **Tick** the **wrong** spellings in the sentence below.

   I heard Dad whistling outside. The wheather was cold so I

   gave him a scarph from the shelf to keep him wharm.

4. **Circle** the three **incorrect** spellings.
   Then spell them correctly on the **lines** underneath.

   She whent to get the microfone but couldn't phind it.

   ....

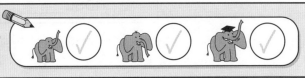

Do 'wh' and 'ph' words make you happy?

Words ending in 'le', 'el', 'al' and 'il'

1. **Circle** the correct **spelling** from each pair of words below.

wobbel / **wobble**   **pencil** / pencel   camil / **camel**

flannel / flannal   hospitle / **hospital**   **cradle** / cradel

2. Draw **lines** to match each gap with the correct word ending.

lent___	le
lev___	el
anim___	al
need___	il

3. **Tick** the correct word ending to complete each word.

word	le	el	al	il
kenn___				
fin___				
eag___				
nostr___				

Words ending in 'le', 'el', 'al' and 'il'

4. **Tick** the **wrong** spellings in the sentences below.

    Jane couldn't wait for the arrivel of the parcal her uncle had

    sent her. She knew it was going to be a jigsaw puzzel.

5. **Circle** the **correct** spelling to complete each sentence below.

    The **castel / castle** is famous for its secret passages.

    Ben used a **shovel / shoval** to clear the driveway.

    That breed of dog is very **loyal / loyel**.

6. **Write** either '**le**', '**el**' or '**il**' in each gap below to complete the sentence.

    The **hot**.............. they were staying in was very posh.

    My birthday is in **Apr**.............. and so is my best friend's.

    Mum made a delicious **trif**.............. for pudding.

Are you smiling like a Spellephant?

Adding 'ing', 'ed', 'er', 'est' and 'y'

1. **Circle** the word that is spelt **correctly**.

lookking   moodyest   muddy   huried   joger

2. **Circle** the **correct** spelling in each pair of words below.

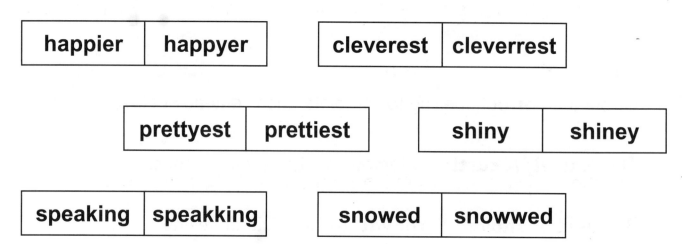

happier	happyer

cleverest	cleverrest

prettyest	prettiest

shiny	shiney

speaking	speakking

snowed	snowwed

3. **Circle** the **correct** spelling to complete each sentence below.

The missing ball was **buried / buryed** under a pile of leaves.

Her dad was busy **slicing / sliceing** onions for their tea.

I took my **dirtey / dirty** boots off before going in the house.

Adding 'ing', 'ed', 'er', 'est' and 'y'

4. **Circle** the **incorrect** spellings in the passage below.

My new bed is the comfyest I have ever owned. It is

softer than my old one and makes me feel very sleeppy.

5. Add '**ed**' to the words below. You may need to add or remove other letters.

nod............ **slip**............ **stare**............

6. Add the ending in the box to the word next to it. You might need
   to change some letters. The first one has been done for you.

glide ⇒ | Add 'ing' | ⇒ ....**gliding**............

marry ⇒ | Add 'ed' | ⇒ ....

silly ⇒ | Add 'er' | ⇒ ....

lovely ⇒ | Add 'est' | ⇒ ....

laze ⇒ | Add 'y' | ⇒ ....

Are you as skilful as a Spellephant?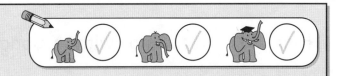

Other rules

1. **Circle** the three **incorrect** spellings.
   Then spell them correctly on the **lines** underneath.

   glove   abov   massive   creative

   live   relativ   nerv   curve

   ....

2. **Circle** the **correct** spelling in each pair of words below.

motion	mosion

solution	solusion

pleasure	pleashure

usual	ushual

posision	position

3. **Circle** the correct word ending to complete each word.

word	word ending	
fi____	z	zz
stea____	l	ll
cla____	s	ss

word	word ending	
hersel____	f	ff
sme____	l	ll
cli____	f	ff

Have you got to grips with this page?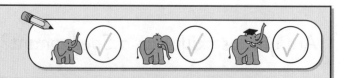

Homophones

1. **Circle** the **correct** spelling to complete each sentence below.

There were only **too / two** biscuits left in the biscuit tin.

She promised she **wood / would** keep my secret safe.

Tina walked to a cafe in town to **meet / meat** her friends.

2. **Write** a word in each box to complete the pairs of homophones.
   The first one has been done for you.

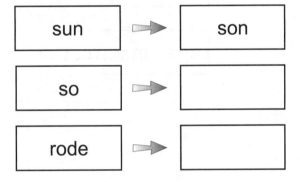

3. **Circle** the **incorrect** spellings in the passage below.

Last night the whether was great so I went four a

walk. I took my camera and got a picture of a dear

buy a tree. I couldn't weight to show it to my mum.

Are you as happy as a Spellephant?

Tricky words

1. **Circle** the correct spelling from each pair of words below.

flor / floor   most / mowst   coud / could

2. Draw **lines** from each word to the correct box in the middle.

Wensday			

Friday

spelt correctly

Tuesday

Munday

spelt incorrectly

Saterday

Sunday

Thersday

3. **Circle** the **incorrect** spellings in the sentences below.
   Then spell them correctly on the **lines** underneath.

The cafe we wanted to eat in was full of peepul.

Sally was sad that she didn't see eny tigers at the zoo.

....

Tricky words

4. **Unscramble** the letters in each circle to make a word.
    Write the word on the line below each circle.

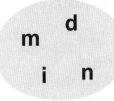

....

5. **Write** the **correct** spellings of the underlined words on each line.

| He fell into the pond <u>agen</u>. |

....

| My friend couldn't <u>fynd</u> her diary. |

....

| John had <u>stayk</u> for his dinner. |

....

6. Find the **three incorrect** spellings in the passage below.
    Write the correct spellings on each line.

    I saved up all the monee I got for Krismas this year.

    Then my pairents took me shopping so I could spend it.

    ....

How tricky do you find tricky words?

Section 4 — Spelling

Mixed practice

1. **Circle** the **correct** spelling to complete each sentence below.

They are building a garage on the **side / syde** of their house.

My left **foot / fut** is sore after our long walk yesterday.

I am **afrade / afraid** that I won't be picked for the netball team.

2. **Circle** the word that is spelt **correctly** in each pair.

skin	scin
mok	mock

engine	endgine
dolfin	dolphin

phool	fool
dise	dice

3. **Circle** the **correct** spelling from each pair of words below.

crutch / cruch   knew / gnew   latch / lach

fech / fetch   arch / artch   nose / knose

4. Put a **tick** in the boxes next to the words that are spelt **correctly**.

foggy ☐   timeing ☐   spied ☐

grabbed ☐   wisest ☐   dryest ☐

Mixed practice

5. Use each word in the boxes **once** to complete the passage.

sore	whole	hole	saw

I .... my pet rabbit eat a .... carrot.

Then he went to sit in a .... he made in the garden.

I think he might have a .... stomach.

6. Draw a **line** from each word below to the correct heading.

| civil |

| magicle | | spelt correctly | | barrel |

| triangle | | spelt incorrectly | | rumbel |

| normel | | rebel |

| gerbal |

It's the last page! Are you a Spellephant?

Glossary

Adjective		A word that tells you more about a noun — **big** cat, **red** ball.
Adverb		A word that describes a verb — He walked **quickly**.
Apostrophe	'	Used to show where letters are missing in a word — isn't. Also used to show who something belongs to — Tim's hat.
Capital letter		Used at the start of sentences. Also used at the start of names of people, places and days of the week, and for 'I'.
Comma	,	Separates items in a list — apples, oranges and bananas.
Command		A sentence which gives an order — **Sit at the table.**
Exclamation		A sentence which starts with 'what' or 'how' and shows strong feelings — **What a great meal that was!**
Exclamation mark	!	Used at the end of sentences showing strong feelings. Also used at the end of some commands — **Stop doing that!**
Full stop	.	Used to show the end of a sentence — I am thirsty.
Noun		A word that names something — **Paul**, **hamster**, **table**.
Noun phrase		A group of words including a noun and other words which give more information about the noun — **the heavy bag**.
Plural		More than one of something — **dogs**, **boxes**, **carrots**.

E2G11